EUREKA MATH²®

A Story of Units®

Ten Tens ▸ 2

APPLY

GREAT MINDS™

Great Minds® is the creator of *Eureka Math*®,
Wit & Wisdom®, *Alexandria Plan*™, and *PhD Science*®.

Published by Great Minds PBC.
greatminds.org

Printed in the USA
B-Print

3 4 5 6 7 8 9 10 11 12 QDG 27 26 25 24 23

ISBN 978-1-64497-644-9

Contents

Shapes and Time with Fraction Concepts

FAMILY MATH
Attributes of Geometric Shapes

Dear Family,

Your student is learning that geometry is the study of shapes, solids, and the parts that make them. They name two-dimensional shapes by identifying attributes, such as the number of sides or angles. They learn that polygons are closed shapes with three or more straight sides, and the number of sides equals the number of angles. Your student learns that quadrilaterals can be classified by characteristics, such as parallel sides and right angles. They build a cube and learn that it is a three-dimensional shape made up of six squares.

Key Terms

angle

right angle

vertex

Pentagon

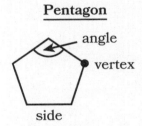

A pentagon is a polygon with five sides and angles. Two sides meet to form an angle, and the point at which they meet is called a vertex.

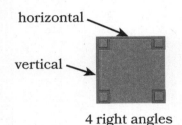

4 right angles

A right angle is an angle with square corners.

opposite sides parallel

A parallelogram is a quadrilateral with opposite sides that are parallel. Squares, rectangles, trapezoids, and rhombuses are all examples of parallelograms.

Cube

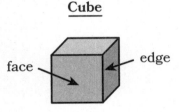

A cube has 6 square faces, or flat parts. When two faces meet, they form an edge.

At-Home Activities

Guess My Polygon

Play a guessing game with your student. Draw a shape and keep it hidden from each other. Take turns asking yes or no questions to guess what shape the other person drew.

- "Does your polygon have 3 sides?"
- "Does your polygon have 4 angles?"
- "Does your polygon have 2 pairs of parallel sides?"

I See Parallel Lines and Right Angles

Explore rooms of your house to identify objects that have two pairs of parallel sides and four right angles. You may point out doorframes, windows, TVs, or books. Consider taking a walk outside with your student to find other objects with these attributes.

1

Name

1. Circle the closed shapes.

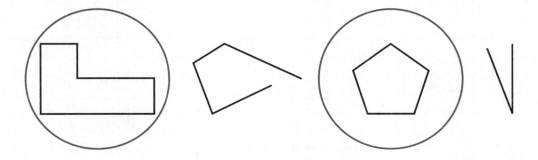

> **Geometry** is the study of shapes, solids, and the parts that make them.
>
> **Attributes** are characteristics that describe a shape.

> A closed shape has no gaps between the sides.
>
> **Sides** are the parts of a line that show the outer border of a shape.
>
> When two sides meet, they create an **angle**.
>
> The point where two sides meet is called a **vertex**.

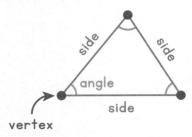

2. Draw a polygon.　Sample:

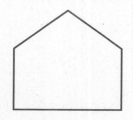 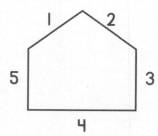 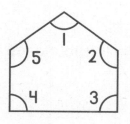

A **polygon** is a closed shape that has straight sides.

I know a polygon has the same number of sides as the number of angles.

There are no gaps or overlaps where the sides meet.

I draw a polygon that has 5 sides and 5 angles.

REMEMBER

Add. Show how you know.

3. 146 + 35 = _181_

146 needs 4 to make the next ten.

I break apart 35 into 4 and 31.

146 + 35 = ____

         /\
        4 31

I add 4 and 146 to make 150.

Then I add 150 and 31.

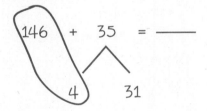

146 + 35 = ——

         4   31

146 + 4 + 31

150 + 31

Name

1. Circle the closed shapes.

2. Write the number of sides and angles.

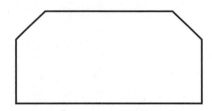 

_____ sides _____ angles   _____ sides _____ angles

3. Draw a polygon.

REMEMBER

Add. Show how you know.

4. $167 + 15 =$ _____

Name

Draw a line to match.

1. hexagon

2. triangle

3. quadrilateral

4. pentagon

I count the sides and angles to name a polygon.

I count 5 sides and 5 angles.

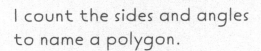

This polygon is a pentagon.

A triangle has 3 sides and 3 angles.

A **quadrilateral** has 4 sides and 4 angles.

A **pentagon** has 5 sides and 5 angles.

A hexagon has 6 sides and 6 angles.

5. Beth draws two shapes. She says both shapes are hexagons.

   Is she correct?

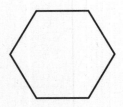 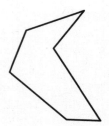

Tell how you know. Sample:

Yes, Beth is correct because both shapes have 6 sides and 6 angles.

Both shapes have 6 sides and 6 angles.

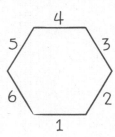 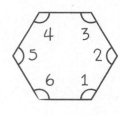

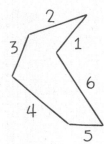 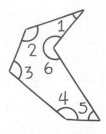

They are both hexagons even though they look different.

2

Name _____

Draw a line to match.

1. hexagon

2. triangle

3. quadrilateral

4. pentagon

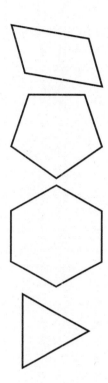

5. Ling draws two shapes. She says both shapes are quadrilaterals.

   Is she correct?

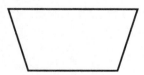 |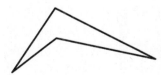

   Tell how you know.

   _____

   _____

Name _____

1. Circle pairs of parallel lines.

Horizontal lines go side to side. ———

Vertical lines go up and down.

Parallel lines never cross or touch, even if they keep going.

The pair of blue lines and the pair of yellow lines will never touch. These pairs are parallel.

The orange lines touch. If the green lines keep going, they will touch. Neither pair of lines are parallel.

2. Circle shapes with right angles.

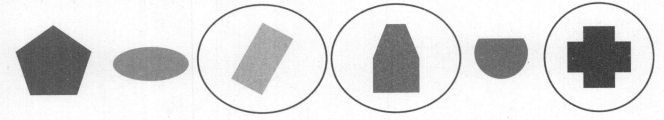

A **right angle** is an angle that has a square corner.

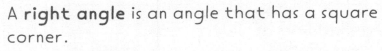

The blue, purple, and yellow shapes have right angles. I can fit a square in at least one of the angles.

gap

There is a gap between the square and the sides of the pentagon, so it does not have right angles.

3. Draw the polygon and write its name.

I have 4 right angles. I have 2 pairs of parallel sides.	Sample:
What am I? Quadrilateral	

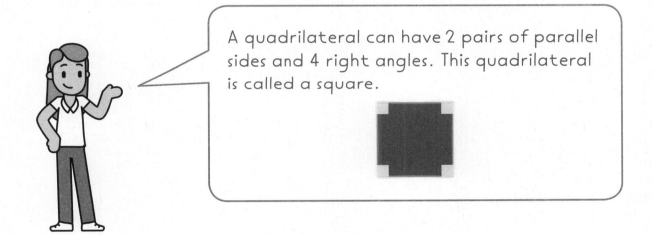

A quadrilateral can have 2 pairs of parallel sides and 4 right angles. This quadrilateral is called a square.

4. Add.

Show how you know.

$$25 + 51 = \underline{76}$$

I decompose each addend into tens and ones.

25   +   51

20 5   50   1

I add the tens together. I add the ones together.

20 + 50 = 70

5 + 1 = 6

Then I combine the tens and ones.

70 + 6 = 76

3

Name

1. Circle pairs of parallel lines.

2. Circle shapes with right angles.

3. Draw the polygon and write its name.

I have 4 right angles. I have 2 pairs of parallel sides.	
What am I? _____	

REMEMBER

4. Add. Show how you know.

$$54 + 35 = \underline{\hspace{2cm}}$$

Name _____

1. Trace the parallel sides. Draw a box to show each right angle.

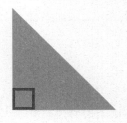
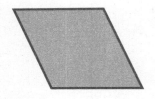

A square will fit in a right angle without gaps between the square and the sides.

The square fits in one of the triangle's angles. This angle is a square corner.

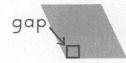

There is a gap between the square and the sides of the rhombus, so its corners are not right angles.

I know lines are parallel if they do not touch, even if I were to keep drawing them.

The sides of the triangle meet. The triangle does not have parallel sides.

The rhombus has 2 pairs of opposite sides that are parallel.

The trapezoid has 1 pair of opposite sides that are parallel.

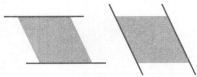

2. Draw each shape. Write two attributes both shapes have.   Sample:

Parallelogram 	Rectangle 
Both shapes have	
4 sides and 2 pairs of opposite sides that are parallel.	

A **parallelogram** is a quadrilateral that has 2 pairs of opposite sides that are parallel.

Both of these shapes are parallelograms.

A rectangle is a parallelogram that has 4 right angles.

Both shapes have 4 sides, 4 angles, and 2 pairs of opposite sides that are parallel.

3. Write the name of each shape.

Sample:

quadrilateral   trapezoid   rhombus

All the shapes have 4 sides and 4 angles, so they are all quadrilaterals.

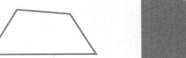

A trapezoid is a quadrilateral with at least 1 pair of parallel sides. This shape can be classified as a trapezoid.

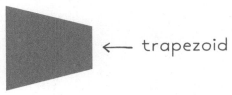
← trapezoid

A rhombus has 4 sides of the same length and 2 pairs of opposite sides that are parallel. This shape can be classified as a rhombus.

← rhombus

Name _____

1. Trace the parallel sides. Draw a box to show each right angle.

2. Draw each shape. Write two attributes both shapes share.

Square	Rhombus

Both shapes have
_____
_____

3. Write the name of each shape.

_____　_____　_____

5

Name

1. Circle the shapes that can make a cube.

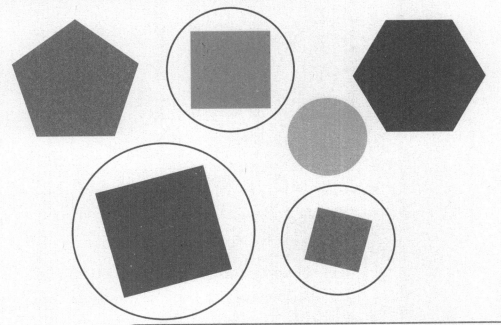

Cubes are made of square faces.

So I circle all the squares.

A **two-dimensional shape** is flat. Its two dimensions are length and width.

A square is a two-dimensional shape.

A **three-dimensional shape** is solid. Its three dimensions are length, width, and height.

Three-dimensional shapes are composed of faces and edges. The **faces** are the flat parts of the solid shape. The **edges** are where two faces meet.

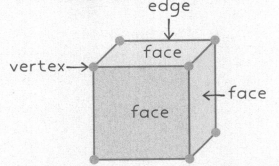

edge

vertex→

face

←face

face

2. Circle the cubes.

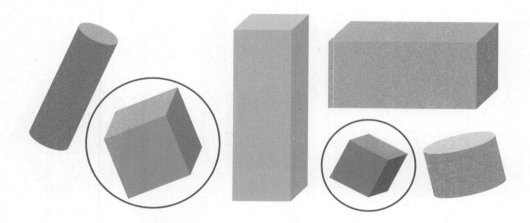

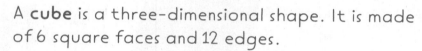

A **cube** is a three-dimensional shape. It is made of 6 square faces and 12 edges.

The orange shape and the red shape are made of square faces. They are cubes.

I see faces that are circles or rectangles on the other shapes, so they are not cubes.

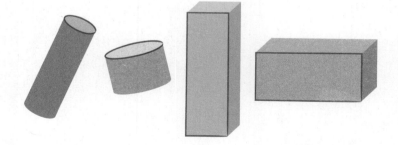

3. Jade says this parallelogram can be 1 face of a cube.

   Is she correct? Show how you know.

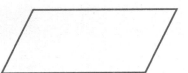

No, Jade is not correct.

The faces of a cube are squares.

The face of a cube is a square.

This parallelogram cannot be the face of a cube because its sides are not equal in length and it does not have square corners like a square.

REMEMBER

4. Write >, =, or < to compare

$$615 \quad = \quad 5 + 600 + 10$$

I can show each total on a place value chart.

100 s	10 s	1s
●●●●● ●	●	●●●●●

615

100 s	10 s	1s
●●●●● ●	●	●●●●●

5 + 600 + 10

There are 6 hundreds 1 ten 5 ones in each.

The totals are equal.

Name

1. Circle the shapes that can make a cube.

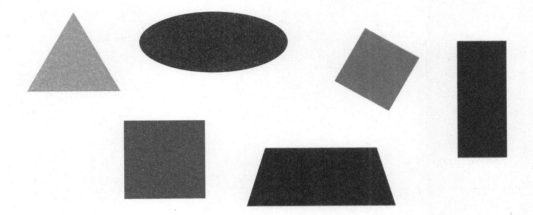

2. Circle the cubes.

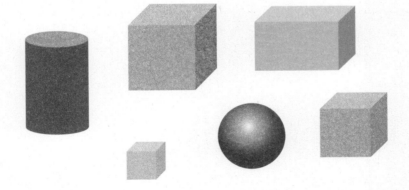

3. Pam says this rectangle can be 1 face of a cube.

    Is she correct? Tell how you know.

    _____

    _____

REMEMBER

4. Write >, =, or < to compare.

832 ⬤ 30 + 2 + 800

FAMILY MATH
Composite Shapes and Fraction Concepts

Dear Family,

Your student is expanding their knowledge of fractions as they learn about relationships between the parts and wholes of shapes. They use pattern blocks to build shapes composed of smaller shapes, called composite shapes. They see that a whole shape can be decomposed, or broken apart, into smaller shapes. Composite shapes build your student's understanding of equal shares. Your student decomposes shapes into units of halves, thirds, and fourths and compares the size of the parts. They see that the more equal parts a shape has, the smaller the parts. This helps prepare them for work with area, fractions, and proportions in later grades.

Key Term

thirds

1 whole hexagon can be decomposed into smaller shapes.

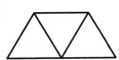

3 triangles can be put together to compose a whole trapezoid.

1 half   1 third   1 fourth

Halves have 2 equal shares.
Thirds have 3 equal shares.
Fourths have 4 equal shares.

It takes 3 thirds to cover 1 whole hexagon. 1 third of the hexagon can be composed with 1 rhombus or 2 triangles.

At-Home Activities

Make Equal Shares

Help your student practice naming halves, thirds, and fourths by slicing food items such as sandwiches, pizza, or brownies. Slice the item into 2, 3, or 4 equal pieces. Discuss whether the pieces are equal and what to name each piece (1 half, 1 third, or 1 fourth), and ask how many pieces are in the whole. Encourage your student to use fraction language to describe the relationship between the parts and the whole (2 halves make 1 whole, 3 thirds make 1 whole, or 4 fourths make 1 whole). As an alternative to food items, modeling clay can be used for this activity.

Make Smaller Shapes

Experiment with different ways to decompose shapes with your student. Start with a piece of paper in the shape of a rectangle or square. Have your student draw lines to split the shape into smaller shapes. Or using a larger surface, such as the top of a table or sidewalk, mark lines with tape or sidewalk chalk. Name the smaller shapes. Then start again and ask your student to decompose the shape a different way.

- "1 whole square can be decomposed into 4 smaller squares, 4 triangles, 2 triangles, or 2 rectangles."

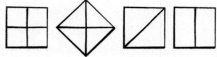

- "1 whole rectangle can be decomposed into 4 squares, 4 triangles, or 2 smaller rectangles."

6

Name

1. Ming decomposed the trapezoid into smaller shapes.

He made 3 triangles.

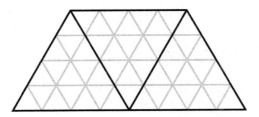

Show two more ways to decompose the trapezoid into smaller shapes.

Then name the shapes you made.

I can cut out pattern blocks and place them on top of the trapezoid to find smaller polygons that fit inside it.

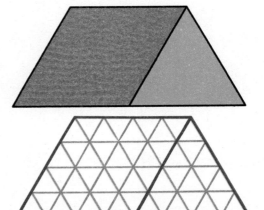

I can also visualize, or think about, smaller shapes that will fit inside the trapezoid.

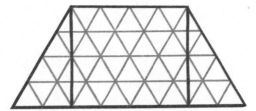

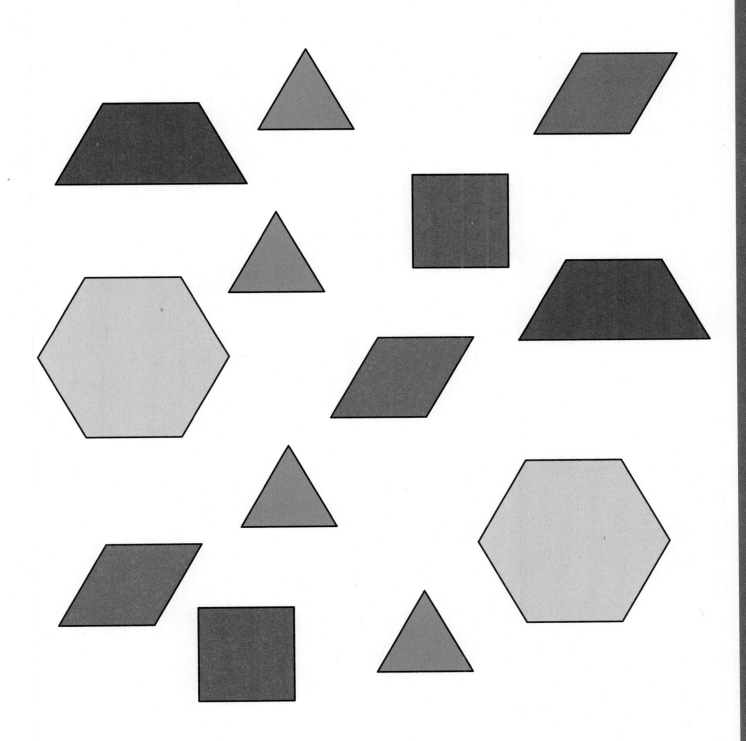

6

Name

Cut out the pattern blocks.

1. Lee decomposed the rhombus into smaller shapes.

   He made 1 trapezoid and 2 triangles.

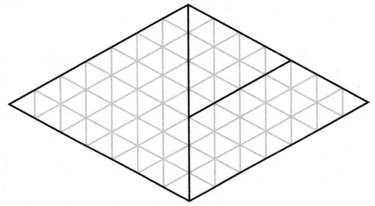

   Show two more ways to decompose the rhombus into smaller shapes.

   Then name the shapes you made.

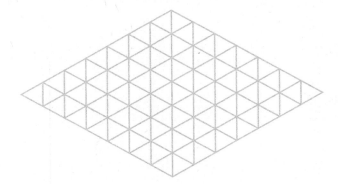

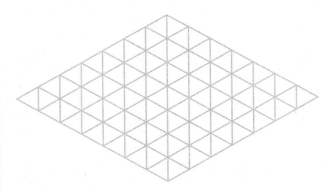

I decomposed the rhombus into

I decomposed the rhombus into

_____

_____

_____

_____

Name _____

Name the composed polygon.

1.

2.

Sample:

3.

Sample:

triangle   **trapezoid**   **rectangle**

A composed polygon is made up of smaller shapes.

I trace and count the sides of the composed polygons.

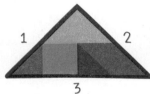

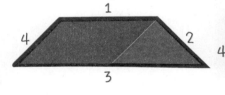

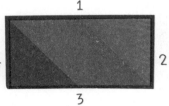

The first shape has 3 sides, so it is a triangle.

The second shape has 4 sides and 1 pair of opposite sides that are parallel, so it can be classified as a trapezoid.

The third shape has 4 sides and 4 right angles, so it can be classified as a rectangle.

4. Trace three tangram pieces to make a quadrilateral with 2 pairs of opposite sides that are parallel.　Sample:

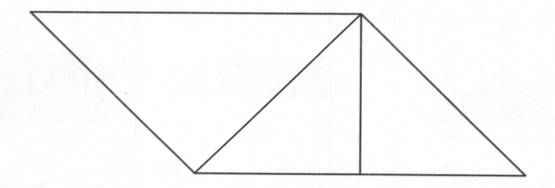

Parallel sides never cross or touch even if they continue.

I flip and turn my tangram pieces until I have composed a shape with 2 pairs of opposite sides that are parallel.

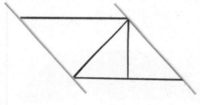　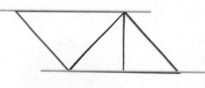

REMEMBER

5. Circle all the shapes with parallel sides.

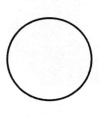  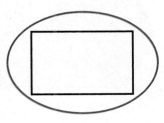

The circle does not have straight sides, so it cannot have parallel sides.

The rectangle and rhombus have straight sides. I draw lines to extend the sides of each shape to see if they will ever cross or touch.

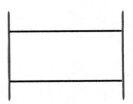 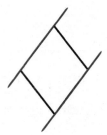

They will never cross or touch, so the rectangle and the rhombus have parallel sides.

　　　　　　　　　　　　　PRACTICE PARTNER 　　43

6. Trace a composed shape.   Sample:

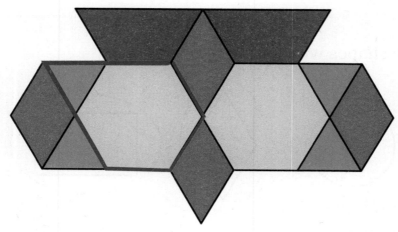

How many sides does the composed shape have? _____5_____

Circle the shapes that make the composed shape.

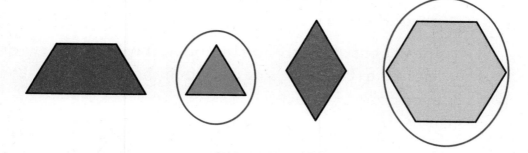

A composed shape is made of two or more different shapes.

I trace a hexagon and a triangle to compose a new shape.

The new shape has 5 sides, so it is a pentagon.

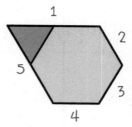

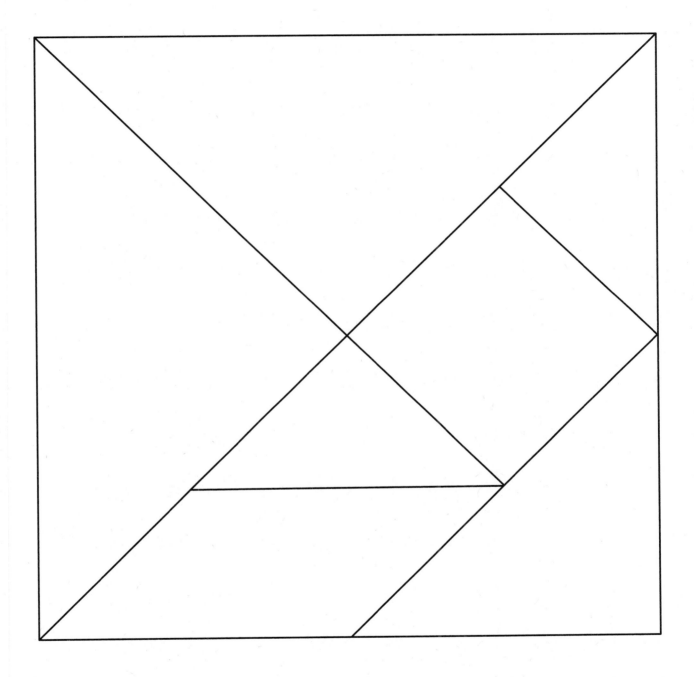

Name

Cut out the tangram pieces.

Name the composed polygon.

1.

2.

3.

_____ _____ _____

4. Trace two tangram pieces to make a quadrilateral with 2 pairs of parallel sides.

Write the name of the quadrilateral. _____

REMEMBER

5. Circle the shapes with parallel sides.

6. Trace a composed shape.

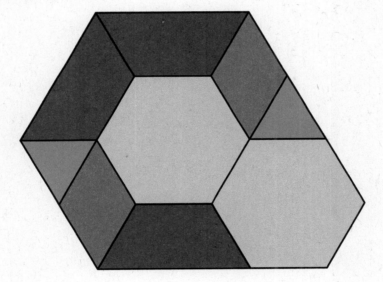

How many sides does the composed shape have? _____

Circle the shapes that make the composed shape.

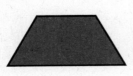  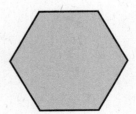

Name

1. Circle the shapes with 4 equal parts.

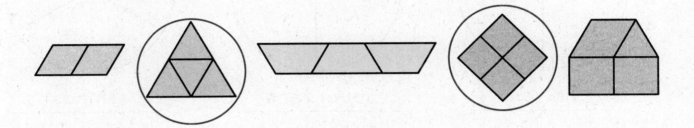

I count the number of parts in each shape.

  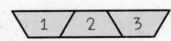

The orange, purple, and red shapes have 4 parts.

The red shape's parts are not all equal.

The orange and purple shapes each have 4 equal parts.

2. Label each shape as halves, thirds, or quarters.

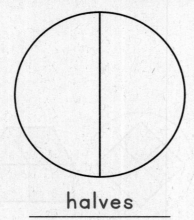   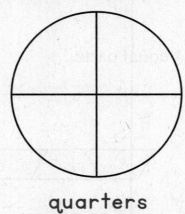   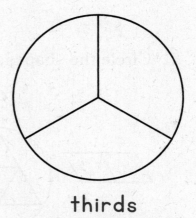

halves   quarters   thirds
_____   _____   _____

I count the number of units used to make each shape.

2 equal parts, or units, are called halves.

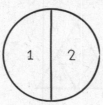

4 equal parts, or units, are called fourths or quarters.

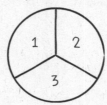

3 equal parts, or units, are called thirds.

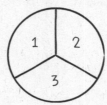

3. What unit describes the parts of this trapezoid?

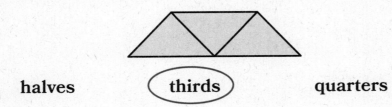

halves   (thirds)   quarters

I count the number of parts in the shape.

There are 3 parts.

All of the parts are the same size, so they are equal.

I know 3 equal parts are called **thirds**.

Name

1. Circle the shapes with 3 equal parts.

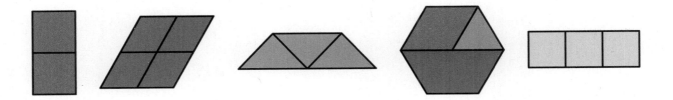

2. Label each shape as halves, thirds, or fourths.

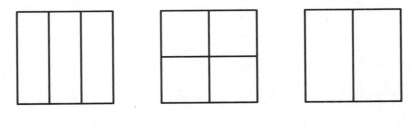

_____   _____   _____

3. What unit describes the parts of this triangle?

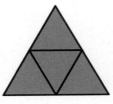

halves   thirds   quarters

Name

Circle the shape that shows each share.

1. 1 third of the whole

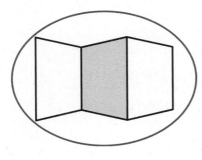 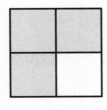 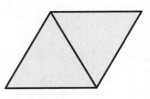

I know 1 third is 1 of 3 equal parts.

I count the number of units used to make each shape.

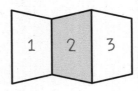

The first shape has 1 of 3 equal parts shaded, so this shape shows 1 third of 1 whole.

The other shapes show more or fewer than 3 equal parts, so they do not show thirds.

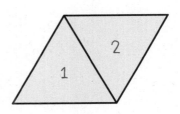

2. Partition the hexagon into thirds. Shade 1 third. Sample:

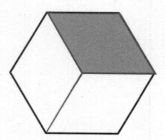

What shape is 1 third of the hexagon? _____a rhombus_____

I know thirds are 3 equal parts.

I think about trying to use 3 of the same pattern block to compose a hexagon.

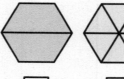

It only takes 2 trapezoids to compose a hexagon, so I can't use trapezoids to partition the hexagon into thirds.

It takes 6 triangles to compose a hexagon, so I can't use triangles to partition the hexagon into thirds.

3 rhombuses compose a hexagon, so I partition the hexagon into 3 equal parts by drawing 3 rhombuses.

Then I shade 1 part to show 1 third of the shape.

REMEMBER

3. What is the difference in length?

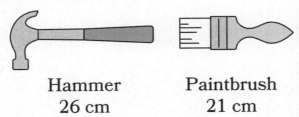

Hammer
26 cm

Paintbrush
21 cm

Show the difference in length two ways. Write an equation for each way.

The difference in length is __5__ cm.

I draw a tape diagram to show the lengths of the hammer and the paintbrush.

| H | 26 |
| P | 21 |

I think about how many more centimeters the paintbrush needs to equal the length of the hammer.

I count on from 21 to 26 and label the difference.

| H | 26 |
| P | 21 | 5 |

21 + 5 = 26

I can also think, "How much longer is the hammer than the paintbrush?"

26
| H | 21 2̶6̶ | 5 |
| P | 21 |

I can subtract the length of the paintbrush from the length of the hammer to find the difference.

26 – 21 = 5

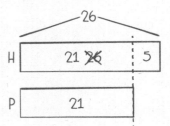

9

Name

1. Circle the shape that shows each share.

1 half of the whole

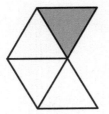 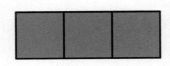

1 fourth of the whole

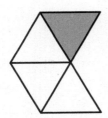 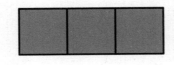

2. Partition the trapezoid into thirds. Shade 1 third.

What shape is 1 third of the trapezoid? _____

REMEMBER

3. What is the difference in length?

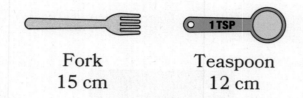

Fork
15 cm

Teaspoon
12 cm

Show the difference in length two ways.

Write an equation for each way.

The difference in length is _____ cm.

FAMILY MATH
Halves, Thirds, and Fourths of Circles and Rectangles

Dear Family,

Your student is building their understanding of fractions by partitioning circles and rectangles into equal parts. They see that fractional parts are only equal if they are from the same-size whole. They discover that halves of a square or rectangle can be different shapes, but halves of a circle are always the same shape. Your student compares the size of the parts when shapes are partitioned into halves, thirds, and fourths. They learn that when there are more equal parts in a whole, the parts are smaller. They combine a known part with an unknown part to compose 1 whole and describe the whole by the number of equal parts. Your student learns that two parts from the same-size rectangle can be different shapes and still be equal parts.

Key Term

fraction

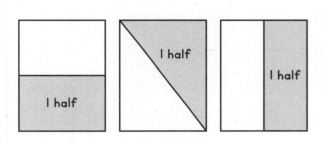

Each rectangle is partitioned into halves. One fraction, or equal part, of the rectangle is 1 half. 1 half and 1 half make 1 whole.

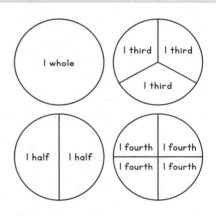

1 fourth is smaller than 1 half of the same whole because there are more equal parts. That means each part is smaller.

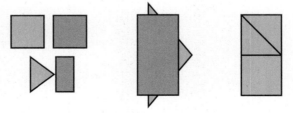

Equal parts of the same-size square or rectangle can be different shapes.

At-Home Activity

Equal Parts in Our World

Encourage your student to use the terms *halves*, *thirds*, and *fourths* to describe equal parts and wholes in everyday situations.

- "Our pizza is partitioned into two equal parts. One part has peppers. What fraction of the pizza has peppers?" (1 half) "What fraction of the pizza does not have peppers?" (1 half) "How many halves is the whole pizza?" (2 halves)

- "The kitchen window is divided equally into 4 panes. What fraction of the window does each pane represent?" (1 fourth) "How many fourths is the whole window?" (4 fourths)

- "This cherry pie is partitioned into 3 equal slices. What does one slice represent?" (1 third) "How many more slices do I need to make 1 whole?" (2 thirds) "How many thirds is the whole pie?" (3 thirds)

Name _____

1. Circle the shapes that show 2 equal shares.

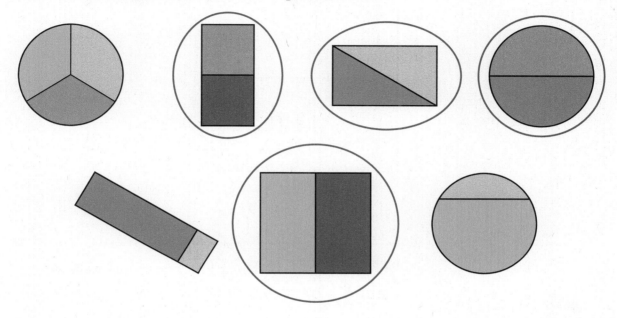

2 equal shares is the same as 2 equal parts.

The unit that describes 2 equal parts is halves.

I look for and circle the shapes that are split into 2 equal parts.

The other shapes have more than 2 parts or have 2 parts that are not equal.

2. Partition the shape into halves. Shade and label 1 half.

I half

I think about folding the rectangle into 2 equal parts, or halves.

I draw a line where the fold would be.

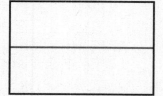

The rectangle is now partitioned into 2 equal parts.

I shade and label 1 part to show 1 half.

10

Name

1. Circle the shapes that show 2 equal shares.

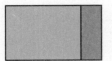

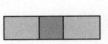

2. What unit describes the 2 equal parts of this shape?

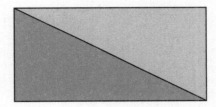

3. Partition each shape into halves. Shade and label 1 half.

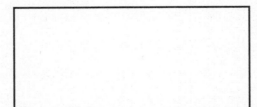

Name

1. Partition each shape and shade 1 unit.

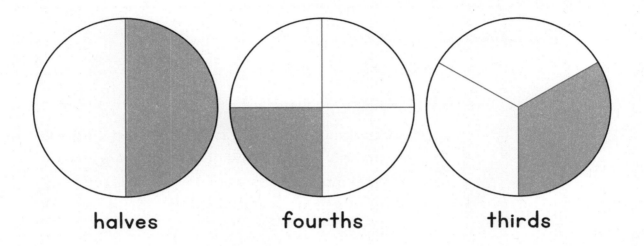

halves   fourths   thirds

I partition the first circle into 2 equal shares to show halves. I shade 1 half.

I partition the next circle into 4 equal shares to show fourths. I shade 1 fourth.

I partition the last circle into 3 equal shares to show thirds. I shade 1 third.

2. Matt wants a big piece of a brownie.

   Pam says to cut the brownie into halves.

   Matt says cutting the brownie into fourths will make bigger pieces.

   Who is correct? _____ Pam _____

   Show how you know.

I can draw and partition a square into 2 equal parts, or halves, to show how Pam is thinking about cutting the brownie.

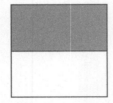

Then I can draw and partition a square into 4 equal parts, or fourths, to show how Matt is thinking about cutting the brownie. I make sure both brownies are the same size.

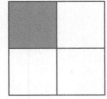

I can see that a brownie cut into halves makes bigger pieces than a brownie cut into fourths.

REMEMBER

Cut out the 10 cm ruler.

3. Use the 10 cm ruler to measure.

   The paintbrush is ___7 cm___ long.

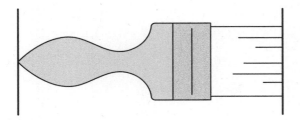

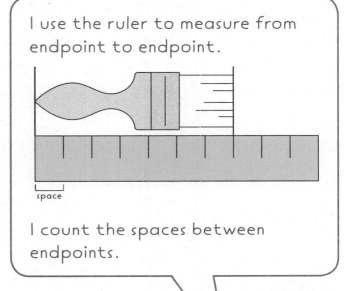

> I use the ruler to measure from endpoint to endpoint.
>
> I count the spaces between endpoints.

4. Subtract. Show how you know.

   92 − 68 = ___24___

   Sample:

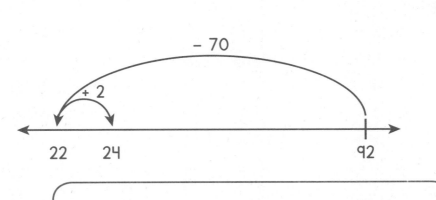

> 68 is close to the benchmark number 70.
>
> So first I subtract 70 from 92.
>
> I subtracted 2 too many, so I add back 2.

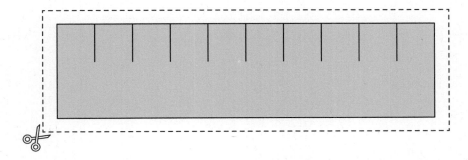

🖊 **11**

Name _____

1. Partition each shape and shade 1 unit.

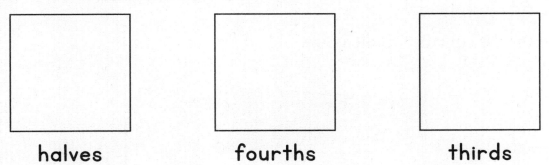

halves   fourths   thirds

2. Kevin wants a big slice of cake.

   Ming says to cut the cake into fourths.

   Kevin says cutting the cake into halves will make bigger slices.

   Who is correct? _____

   Show how you know.

REMEMBER

Cut out the 10 cm ruler.

3. Use the 10 cm ruler to measure.

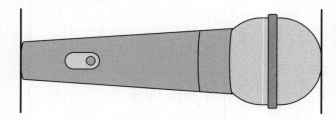

The microphone is _____ long.

4. Subtract. Show how you know.

$$64 - 37 = \underline{\hspace{1cm}}$$

12

Name

Name the shaded part of the shape.

1.

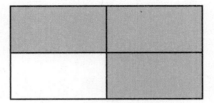

3 fourths

The shape is partitioned into 4 equal parts, or fourths.

3 of the 4 parts are shaded.

So 3 fourths of the shape are shaded.

Write the fraction that makes 1 whole.

2.

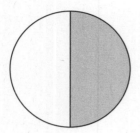

1 half
_____

3.

2 thirds
_____

A **fraction** tells how many equal parts make a whole.

2 halves make 1 whole.

1 half is shaded. So I need 1 half more to make 1 whole.

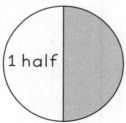

1 half

3 thirds make 1 whole.

1 third is shaded. So I need 2 thirds more to make 1 whole.

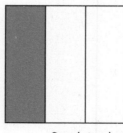

2 thirds

Name

Name the shaded part of the shape.

1.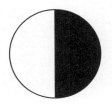

2.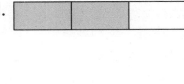

3.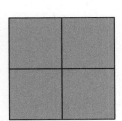

_____

Write the fraction that makes 1 whole.

4.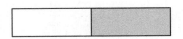

5.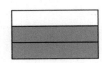

_____

6.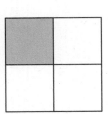

7.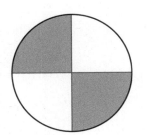

_____

Name

Show equal shares. Partition each shape two ways.

1. halves

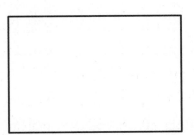 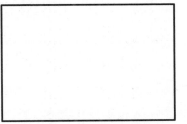

I think about folding each rectangle into 2 equal shares, or parts, to show halves.

I draw a line where the fold would be.

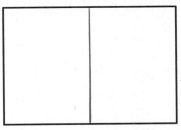 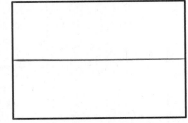

I could also make halves by drawing from the top corner to the opposite bottom corner. The equal parts would be 2 triangles.

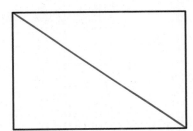

2. fourths

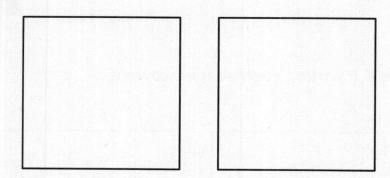

I think about folding each square into 4 equal shares, or parts, to show fourths.

I draw lines where the folds would be.

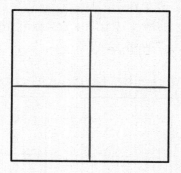

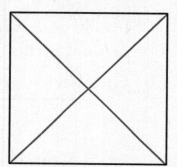

REMEMBER

3. **Read**

   Mr. Webb has 41 tomatoes.

   He uses some tomatoes to make sauce.

   He has 19 tomatoes left.

   How many tomatoes does
   Mr. Webb use?

   Draw

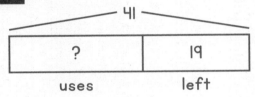

I read the problem.

I read again. As I reread, I think about what I can draw.

I draw and label a tape diagram to show the number of tomatoes.

I am trying to find how many tomatoes Mr. Webb uses. I know one part and the total, so I can subtract 19 from 41 to find the other part.

19 is close to the benchmark number 20, so I can use compensation to subtract.

First, I subtract 20 from 41. I can use the arrow way to show my thinking.

$$41 \xrightarrow{\;-\;20\;} 21 \xrightarrow{\;+\;1\;} 22$$

I subtracted 1 too many, so I add back 1.

Write Sample:

$$41 - 19 = 22$$

Mr. Webb uses ___22___ tomatoes.

13

Name _____

Show equal shares. Partition each shape two ways.

1. fourths

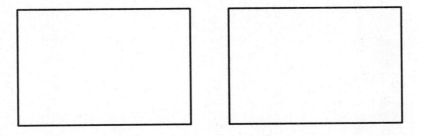

2. thirds

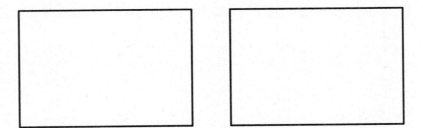

3. halves

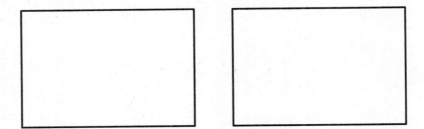

REMEMBER

4. **Read**

Miss Wells picks 65 apples.

She uses some of the apples to bake pies.

She has 27 apples left.

How many apples does Miss Wells use?

Draw

Write

Miss Wells uses _____ apples.

FAMILY MATH
Application of Fractions to Tell Time

Dear Family,

Your student is using their knowledge of halves and fourths to learn to tell time to the nearest 5 minutes. They begin by looking at a timeline of a day to see that 24 hours can be divided into 2 equal halves, labeled a.m. and p.m. They perform tasks that help them realize 60 seconds compose 1 minute and 60 minutes compose 1 hour. Your student folds a paper circle into fourths, or quarters, to create a clock and identifies quarter past the hour and quarter to the next hour. They relate minutes on a clock to a number line. Each interval, or gap, on the number line represents 5 minutes. This connection helps your student make sense of how the hour hand moves in relation to the minute hand.

Key Terms

quarter past

quarter to

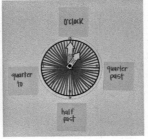

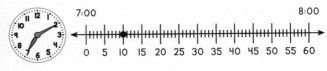

It only takes about a second to take a picture, but it probably takes a minute to brush my teeth.

Thinking about the clock split into 2 or 4 equal parts helps to understand what fraction of the hour has passed.

This minute hand points to the number that tells how many 5-minute intervals have gone by. As each minute passes, the next hour gets closer. The hour hand moves to show the progress.

At-Home Activities

How Long?

Help your student choose the correct unit of time to estimate how long it takes to do familiar activities. Ask them if they would use seconds, minutes, or hours to describe how long the activity takes.

- "You went to bed at 8:00 p.m. and woke up at 7:00 a.m. Do we use seconds, minutes, or hours to say how long you slept?"

- "Do we use seconds, minutes, or hours to describe how long it takes to walk to school?"

- "I wonder how long it takes to pick up your toys. Do we measure that amount of time in seconds, minutes, or hours?"

What Time Is It?

Discuss the time of daily activities to help your student practice describing the meaning of *quarter to*, *quarter past*, and *half past* and distinguishing between a.m. and p.m.

- "We eat supper at half past 5:00. What time do we eat supper?" (5:30) "Is that a.m. or p.m.?" (p.m.)

- "Your bedtime is at quarter to 9:00. What time do you go to bed?" (8:45) "Is that a.m. or p.m.?" (p.m.)

- "School starts at a quarter past 7:00. What time does school start?" (7:15) "Is that a.m. or p.m.?" (a.m.)

14

Name

Circle a.m. or p.m. for each picture.

1. **2:30**

a.m.   (p.m.)

2. **7:00**

(a.m.)   p.m.

The morning hours are known as a.m. They begin at 12:00 a.m., or midnight, while we are sleeping and end at 12:00 p.m., or noon, around lunchtime.

Afternoon and evening hours are known as p.m. They start at noon and end at midnight.

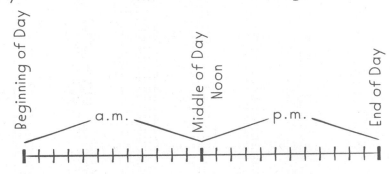

The children are on the playground at 2:30. They would be sleeping at 2:30 a.m., so it must be 2:30 p.m.

The students are getting on the school bus at 7:00. School is over by 7:00 p.m., so it must be 7:00 a.m.

14

Name

Circle a.m. or p.m. for each picture.

1.   7:30

a.m.   p.m.

2.   3:30

a.m.   p.m.

3.   6:00

a.m.   p.m.

4.   11:00

a.m.   p.m.

15

Name

Circle the unit of time to measure each task.

1.　　　　Sleep at night.　　　　2.　　　　Take a sip of water.

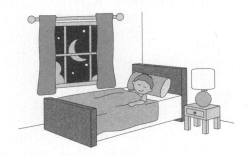　　　　

seconds　minutes　(hours)　　(seconds)　minutes　hours

Seconds are the shortest unit of time.

There are 60 seconds in 1 minute.

Hours are longer than seconds or minutes.

There are 60 minutes in 1 hour.

I think about how long each task takes.

I sleep for more than a few minutes at night, so I circle hours.

It takes less than a minute to take a sip of water, so I circle seconds.

Draw a picture for each unit of time. Then write a sentence.

3. What task takes about 1 minute? Sample:

Tying my shoes takes about

1 minute.

I think about things I can do in about 1 minute, or 60 seconds.

REMEMBER

4. Use the number line to subtract.

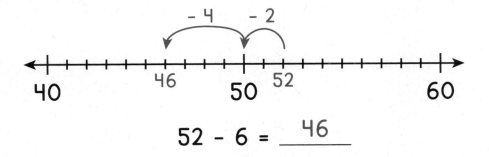

$$52 - 6 = \underline{\quad 46 \quad}$$

I start at the total, 52, on the number line.

I need to subtract 6.

First, I hop back 2 to get to the benchmark number, 50.

Then, I hop back 4 more.

15

Name

Circle the unit of time to measure each task.

1. Eat your lunch.

seconds   minutes   hours

2. Go down the slide.

seconds   minutes   hours

Draw a picture for each unit of time. Then write a sentence.

3. What task takes about 1 hour?

_____

_____

_____

_____

REMEMBER

4. Use the number line to subtract.

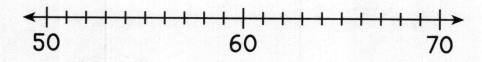

$$65 - 8 = \underline{\hspace{2cm}}$$

💬 **16**

Name

Write the time.

1.

___6:15___

2.

___6:45___

On the first clock, the hour hand is a little past the 6.

The minute hand is pointing at the 3. It shows that 1 quarter of 1 hour has passed.

1 quarter

I know 1 quarter of 1 hour is 15 minutes.

I write the hour and then I write the minutes.

hour:minute
6:15

The shorter hand on the clock is the hour hand.

The longer hand on the clock is the minute hand.

On the second clock, the hour hand is closer to the 7.

The minute hand is pointing to the 9. It shows that 3 quarters of 1 hour have passed.

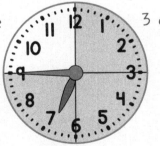

3 quarters

I know 3 quarters of 1 hour is 45 minutes.

I write the hour and then I write the minutes.

hour:minute
6:45

Draw the missing hand on each clock to show the time.

3.

quarter to 8:00

4.

half past 1:00

5.

quarter past 5:00

Quarter to means the minute hand is 3 quarters, or 3 fourths, of the way around the clock.

The minute hand points to the 9 at quarter to the next hour.

So I draw the minute hand pointing to the 9.

Quarter past means the minute hand is 1 quarter, or 1 fourth, of the way around the clock.

The minute hand points to the 3 at quarter past the hour.

So I draw the minute hand pointing to the 3.

Half past means the minute hand is 2 quarters, or halfway, around the clock.

The minute hand points to the 6 at half past the hour.

So I draw the minute hand pointing to the 6.

/ 16

Name _____

Write the time.

1.

_____

2.
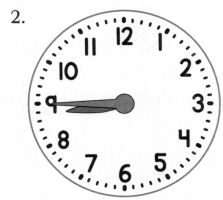

_____

3.

_____

Draw the missing hand on each clock to show the time.

4.

quarter to 2:00

5.

half past 10:00

6.

quarter past 5:00

17

Name

1. Write the time.

7:05

7:40

On the first clock, the hour hand is a little past the 7.

The minute hand is pointing at the 1. I start at the 12 and count by fives until I get to the 1.

I write the hour and then the minutes.

hour:minute
7:05

On the second clock, the hour hand is between the 7 and 8.

The minute hand is pointing at the 8. I start at the 12 and count by fives until I get to the 8.

I write the hour and then the minutes.

hour:minute
7:40

Plot each time on the number line.

<u>7</u> :00

<u>8</u> :00

Both times are between 7:00 and 8:00.
I use those times to label the number line.

The first clock shows the time is 7:05.
I plot a point at the tick mark labeled
5 because it represents 7:05.

The second clock shows the time is 7:40.
I plot a second point at the tick mark
labeled 40 because it represents 7:40.

REMEMBER

Add. Show how you know.

2. 72 + 59 = ___131___

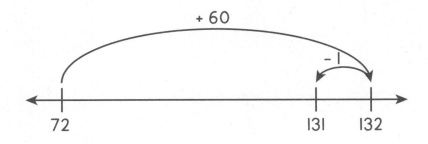

I can use an open number line to show my thinking.

Since 59 is close to a ten, I add 60 to 72.

I know 6 tens and 7 tens is 13 tens.

13 tens is 130 so 60 + 72 = 132.

I added 1 more than I needed, so I subtract 1.

17

Name _____

1. Write the time.

_____   _____

2. Plot each time on the number line.

____:____   ____:____

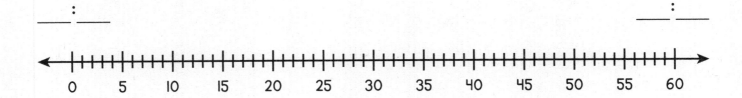

REMEMBER

Add. Show how you know.

3. 84 + 38 = _____

18

Name

Write the time.

1.

2:40

The hour hand is the shorter hand.

The minute hand is the longer hand.

The hour hand is past the 2 but not yet at the 3. So the hour is still 2:00.

The minute hand is pointing at the 8. I start at the 12 and count by fives until I get to the 8.

I write the hour and then the minutes.
hour:minute
2:40

Draw hands on the clock to match the time.

2.

5:25

3.

12:50

On the first clock, I start at the 12 and count by fives to 25. I land on the 5.

I draw the minute hand pointing to the 5.

Since the minute hand is almost halfway around the clock, the hour hand will be about halfway between the hours.

I draw the hour hand pointing halfway between the 5 and the 6.

On the second clock, I start at the 12 and count by fives to 50. I land on the 10.

I draw the minute hand pointing to the 10.

Since the minute hand is almost all the way around the clock, the hour hand will be very close to the next hour.

I draw the hour hand pointing a little before the 1.

/ 18

Name

Write the time.

1.

_____

2.

_____

Draw hands on the clock to match the time.

3.

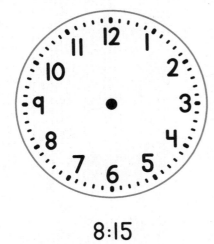

8:15

4.

3:40

Name

1. **Read**

   Kevin starts to clean his room at 2:15 p.m.

   He stops cleaning at 2:45 p.m.

   How long does Kevin clean his room?

   Draw

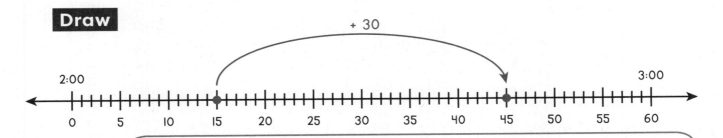

    I read the problem.

   I read again. As I reread, I think about what I can draw.

   I can use the number line to help me organize the information.

   I plot each time on the number line. I plot a point at the tick mark labeled 15 because it represents 2:15. I plot a second point at the tick mark labeled 45 because it represents 2:45.

   I need to find how long Kevin cleans his room. I can use the number line to help me keep track of my count.

   I start at 2:15 and count by fives until I get to 2:45. I count 30 minutes.

   Write

   Kevin cleans his room for 30 minutes.

REMEMBER

2. Circle the cubes.

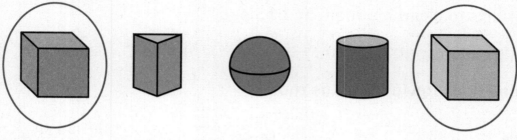

A cube has: _____12_____ edges   _____6_____ faces   _____8_____ vertices

A cube is a three-dimensional shape with 12 edges, 6 faces, and 8 vertices.

A face is the flat part of a three-dimensional shape.

An edge is where 2 faces meet.

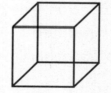

A vertex is where edges meet.

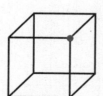

Name

1. **Read**

Alex starts to play basketball at 10:10 a.m.

He stops playing at 10:50 a.m.

How long does Alex play basketball?

Draw

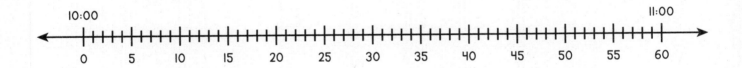

Write

_____

_____

REMEMBER

2. Circle the cubes.

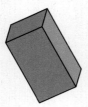 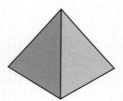 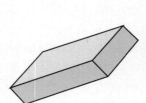 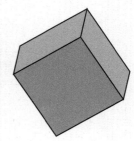

A cube has: _____ edges   _____ faces   _____ vertices

Acknowledgments

Beth Barnes, Dawn Burns, Karla Childs, Mary Christensen-Cooper, Hazel Coltharp, Cheri DeBusk, Stephanie DeGiulio, Jill Diniz, Brittany duPont, Lacy Endo-Peery, Krysta Gibbs, Melanie Gutierrez, Torrie K. Guzzetta, Eddie Hampton, Andrea Hart, Sara Hunt, Rachel Hylton, Travis Jones, Jennifer Koepp Neeley, Liz Krisher, Leticia Lemus, Marie Libassi-Behr, Ben McCarty, Cristina Metcalf, Ashley Meyer, Bruce Myers, Marya Myers, Maximilian Peiler-Burrows, Marlene Pineda, Carolyn Potts, Meri Robie-Craven, Colleen Sheeron-Laurie, Robyn Sorenson, Tara Stewart, Theresa Streeter, James Tanton, Julia Tessler, Philippa Walker, Rachael Waltke, Lisa Watts Lawton, MaryJo Wieland

Trevor Barnes, Brianna Bemel, Adam Cardais, Christina Cooper, Natasha Curtis, Jessica Dahl, Brandon Dawley, Delsena Draper, Sandy Engelman, Tamara Estrada, Soudea Forbes, Jen Forbus, Reba Frederics, Liz Gabbard, Diana Ghazzawi, Lisa Giddens-White, Laurie Gonsoulin, Nathan Hall, Cassie Hart, Marcela Hernandez, Rachel Hirsh, Abbi Hoerst, Libby Howard, Amy Kanjuka, Ashley Kelley, Lisa King, Sarah Kopec, Drew Krepp, Crystal Love, Maya Márquez, Siena Mazero, Cindy Medici, Ivonne Mercado, Sandra Mercado, Brian Methe, Patricia Mickelberry, Mary-Lise Nazaire, Corinne Newbegin, Max Oosterbaan, Tamara Otto, Christine Palmtag, Andy Peterson, Lizette Porras, Karen Rollhauser, Neela Roy, Gina Schenck, Amy Schoon, Aaron Shields, Leigh Sterten, Mary Sudul, Lisa Sweeney, Samuel Weyand, Dave White, Charmaine Whitman, Nicole Williams, Glenda Wisenburn-Burke, Howard Yaffe

Credits

For a complete list of credits, visit http://eurmath.link/media-credits